Maths
made easy

Key Stage 2
ages 9–10
Workbook 1

Author
John Kennedy

Consultant
Sean McArdle

LONDON • NEW YORK • SYDNEY • MOSCOW • DELHI

Reading and writing numbers

264 346 in words is Two hundred and sixty-four thousand, three hundred and forty-six

One million, three hundred and twelve thousand, five hundred and two is 1 312 502

Write each of these numbers in words.

326 208 Three hundred and twenty six thousand two hun & Eight

704 543 Seven hun thou and four thou, five hundel on forty h
          four

240 701 Two hun and forty thou, Seven hundred and one

278 520 Two hun and seventy Eight thousand, five hun and twer

Write each of these in numbers.

Five hundred and seventeen thousand and forty-two   517 042

Six hundred and ninety-four thousand, seven hundred and eleven   694 711

Eight hundred and nine thousand, two hundred and three   809 203

Nine hundred thousand, four hundred and four   900 404

Write each of these numbers in words.

9 307 012

5 042 390

9 908 434

8 400 642

Write each of these in numbers.

Eight million, two hundred and fifty-one

Two million, forty thousand, four hundred and four

Seven million, three hundred and two thousand, one hundred and one

Two million, five hundred and forty-one thousand and five

Multiplying and dividing by 10

Write the answer in the box.

$26 \times 10 = \boxed{260}$

$42 \div 10 = 4\frac{2}{10}$

Write the answer in the box.

$76 \times 10 = 760$ $43 \times 10 = $ $93 \times 10 = $

$66 \times 10 = $ $13 \times 10 = $ $47 \times 10 = $

$147 \times 10 = $ $936 \times 10 = $ $284 \times 10 = $

$364 \times 10 = $ $821 \times 10 = $ $473 \times 10 = $

Write the answer in the box.

$25 \div 10 = $ $17 \div 10 = $ $49 \div 10 = $

$61 \div 10 = $ $33 \div 10 = $ $57 \div 10 = $

$309 \div 10 = $ $247 \div 10 = $ $103 \div 10 = $

$537 \div 10 = $ $893 \div 10 = $ $711 \div 10 = $

Find the number that has been multiplied by 10.

$ \times 10 = 370$ $ \times 10 = 640$ $ \times 10 = 740$

$ \times 10 = 810$ $ \times 10 = 100$ $ \times 10 = 830$

$ \times 10 = 7\,140$ $ \times 10 = 3\,070$ $ \times 10 = 5\,290$

$ \times 10 = 2\,640$ $ \times 10 = 8\,290$ $ \times 10 = 6\,480$

Find the number that has been divided by 10.

$ \div 10 = 3\frac{9}{10}$ $ \div 10 = 2\frac{7}{10}$ $ \div 10 = 9\frac{9}{10}$

$ \div 10 = 42\frac{1}{10}$ $ \div 10 = 93\frac{3}{10}$ $ \div 10 = 74\frac{7}{10}$

$ \div 10 = 57\frac{3}{10}$ $ \div 10 = 38\frac{1}{10}$ $ \div 10 = 86\frac{9}{10}$

Ordering sets of large numbers

Write these numbers in order, starting with the smallest.

2 322	526	404	32	1 240	440
32	404	440	526	1 240	2 322

Write the numbers in each row in order, starting with the smallest.

420	190	950	402	905	986

308	640	380	805	364	910

260	350	26	1 000	620	100

20 500	36 820	2 500	45 600	40 560	25 000

Write the numbers in each row in order, starting with the smallest.

984 000	8 840 000	8 900	98 240	7 560	75 600

301 550	6 405 000	6 450 000	64 500	31 500	3 150

7 000 100	70 100	7 100 000	710	710 000	7 100

TOWN A
Population
85 550

TOWN B
Population
8 550

TOWN C
Population
8 505 420

TOWN D
Population
8 550 042

Which town has:

The largest population?

The second smallest population?

The second largest population?

Rounding numbers

Round these numbers up.

36 to the nearest 10	40
124 to the nearest 100	100
4 360 to the nearest 1 000	4000

Remember if a number is half-way between it is rounded up.

Write these numbers to the nearest 10.

24 is	91 is	55 is	73 is
57 is	68 is	49 is	35 is
82 is	37 is	22 is	52 is
46 is	26 is	85 is	99 is
43 is	51 is	78 is	29 is

Write these numbers to the nearest 100.

386 is	224 is	825 is	460 is
539 is	429 is	378 is	937 is
772 is	255 is	549 is	612 is
116 is	750 is	618 is	990 is
940 is	843 is	172 is	868 is

Write these numbers to the nearest 1 000.

3 240 is	2 500 is	9 940 is	1 051 is
8 945 is	5 050 is	5 530 is	4 850 is
6 200 is	7 250 is	8 499 is	8 450 is
12 501 is	8 762 is	6 500 is	3 292 is
1 499 is	14 836 is	10 650 is	11 241 is

Counting on in constant steps

Continue each row.

Steps of 9:	5	14	23	32	41	50
Steps of 14:	20	34	48	62	76	90

Continue each row.

21	38	55					
13	37	61					
7	25	43					
32	48	64					
12	31	50			107		
32	54	76					186
24	64	104					
4	34	64					
36	126	216		396			
12	72	132					
25	45	65			125		
22	72	122					
25	100	175					
60	165	270			585		
8	107	206					701
10	61	112					
26	127	228					733
48	100	152					

6

Recognising multiples of 6, 7, and 8

Circle the multiples of 6.

8   (12)   15   (18)   20   (24)

Circle the multiples of 6.

8	22	14	18	36	40
16	38	44	25	30	60
6	21	19	54	56	24
12	48	10	20	35	26
42	39	23	28	36	32

Circle the multiples of 7.

7	17	24	59	42	55
15	20	21	46	12	70
14	27	69	36	47	49
65	19	57	28	38	63
33	34	35	37	60	56

Circle the multiples of 8.

40	26	15	25	38	56
26	8	73	41	64	12
75	58	62	24	31	72
12	80	32	46	38	78
16	42	66	28	48	68

Circle the number that is a multiple of 6 *and* 7.

18   54   42   21   28   63

Circle the numbers that are multiples of 6 *and* 8.

16   24   36   48   54   42

Circle the number that is a multiple of 7 *and* 8.

24   32   40   28   42   56

Factors of numbers from 1 to 30

The factors of 10 are   1   2   5   10

Circle the factors of 4   ① ② 3 ④

Write all the factors of these numbers.

The factors of 26 are

The factors of 30 are

The factors of 9 are

The factors of 12 are

The factors of 15 are

The factors of 22 are

The factors of 20 are

The factors of 21 are

The factors of 24 are

Circle all the factors of these numbers.

Which numbers are factors of 14?   1   2   3   5   7   9   12   14

Which numbers are factors of 13?   1   2   3   4   5   6   7   8   9   10   11   13

Which numbers are factors of 7?   1   2   3   4   5   6   7

Which numbers are factors of 11?   1   2   3   4   5   6   7   8   9   10   11

Which numbers are factors of 6?   1   2   3   4   5   6

Which numbers are factors of 8?   1   2   3   4   5   6   7   8

Which numbers are factors of 17?   1   2   5   7   12   14   16   17

Which numbers are factors of 18?   1   2   3   4   5   6   8   9   10   12   18

Some numbers only have factors of 1 and themselves. They are called prime numbers. Write down all the prime numbers that are less than 30 in the box.

Recognising equivalent fractions

Make these fractions equal by putting a number in the box.

$$\frac{1}{2} = \frac{2}{4} \qquad\qquad \frac{1}{3} = \frac{2}{6}$$

Make these fractions equal by putting a number in the box.

$$\frac{1}{2} = \frac{\boxed{}}{10} \qquad \frac{3}{4} = \frac{\boxed{}}{8} \qquad \frac{1}{3} = \frac{\boxed{}}{9}$$

$$\frac{2}{3} = \frac{\boxed{}}{12} \qquad \frac{6}{12} = \frac{\boxed{}}{6} \qquad \frac{4}{8} = \frac{\boxed{}}{2}$$

$$\frac{1}{5} = \frac{\boxed{}}{10} \qquad \frac{4}{12} = \frac{\boxed{}}{6} \qquad \frac{3}{5} = \frac{\boxed{}}{10}$$

$$\frac{1}{4} = \frac{\boxed{}}{8} \qquad \frac{6}{18} = \frac{\boxed{}}{3} \qquad \frac{3}{12} = \frac{\boxed{}}{4}$$

$$\frac{3}{9} = \frac{1}{\boxed{}} \qquad \frac{4}{10} = \frac{2}{\boxed{}} \qquad \frac{3}{4} = \frac{9}{\boxed{}}$$

$$\frac{4}{16} = \frac{1}{\boxed{}} \qquad \frac{15}{20} = \frac{3}{\boxed{}} \qquad \frac{6}{12} = \frac{1}{\boxed{}}$$

$$\frac{3}{5} = \frac{6}{\boxed{}} \qquad \frac{3}{6} = \frac{1}{\boxed{}} \qquad \frac{9}{12} = \frac{3}{\boxed{}}$$

Make these rows of fractions equal by putting a number in each box.

$$\frac{1}{2} = \frac{\boxed{}}{4} = \frac{3}{\boxed{}} = \frac{\boxed{}}{8} = \frac{\boxed{}}{10} = \frac{6}{\boxed{}}$$

$$\frac{1}{4} = \frac{2}{\boxed{}} = \frac{\boxed{}}{12} = \frac{4}{\boxed{}} = \frac{5}{\boxed{}} = \frac{\boxed{}}{24}$$

$$\frac{3}{4} = \frac{6}{\boxed{}} = \frac{\boxed{}}{12} = \frac{12}{\boxed{}} = \frac{\boxed{}}{20} = \frac{18}{\boxed{}}$$

$$\frac{1}{3} = \frac{\boxed{}}{6} = \frac{3}{\boxed{}} = \frac{4}{\boxed{}} = \frac{\boxed{}}{15} = \frac{12}{\boxed{}}$$

$$\frac{1}{5} = \frac{\boxed{}}{10} = \frac{\boxed{}}{15} = \frac{4}{\boxed{}} = \frac{5}{\boxed{}} = \frac{\boxed{}}{30}$$

$$\frac{2}{3} = \frac{\boxed{}}{6} = \frac{\boxed{}}{9} = \frac{8}{\boxed{}} = \frac{10}{\boxed{}} = \frac{14}{\boxed{}}$$

Ordering sets of simple fractions

Put these numbers in order starting with the smallest.

$$2 \qquad 1\frac{1}{2} \qquad \frac{1}{2} \qquad \frac{1}{4} \qquad 1\frac{3}{4}$$

$$\frac{1}{4} \qquad \frac{1}{2} \qquad 1\frac{1}{2} \qquad 1\frac{3}{4} \qquad 2$$

Put these numbers in order starting with the smallest.

$4 \qquad 2\frac{1}{2} \qquad 1\frac{3}{4} \qquad 1\frac{1}{4} \qquad 3\frac{1}{2}$

$2 \qquad 1\frac{1}{2} \qquad 1 \qquad 2\frac{1}{4} \qquad 3$

$2 \qquad 1\frac{1}{4} \qquad 3\frac{1}{2} \qquad 1\frac{1}{2} \qquad 2\frac{1}{2}$

$7\frac{1}{2} \qquad 3\frac{1}{4} \qquad 1\frac{1}{2} \qquad 1\frac{1}{4} \qquad 2\frac{3}{4}$

$4\frac{1}{4} \qquad 3\frac{1}{2} \qquad 2\frac{3}{4} \qquad 2\frac{1}{2} \qquad 3\frac{1}{4}$

$3\frac{3}{4} \qquad 3\frac{1}{3} \qquad 4\frac{1}{4} \qquad 3\frac{2}{3} \qquad 3\frac{1}{2}$

$4\frac{2}{3} \qquad 4\frac{1}{2} \qquad 4\frac{3}{4} \qquad 4\frac{1}{3} \qquad 5\frac{1}{4}$

$7\frac{1}{2} \qquad 6\frac{2}{3} \qquad 7\frac{3}{4} \qquad 7\frac{1}{4} \qquad 6\frac{1}{2}$

$14\frac{1}{2} \qquad 15\frac{3}{4} \qquad 15\frac{1}{2} \qquad 14\frac{3}{4} \qquad 13\frac{3}{4}$

$7\frac{1}{3} \qquad 8\frac{1}{2} \qquad 7\frac{3}{4} \qquad 8\frac{1}{5} \qquad 7\frac{2}{3}$

$10\frac{1}{5} \qquad 9\frac{3}{4} \qquad 10\frac{1}{2} \qquad 9\frac{1}{5} \qquad 9\frac{1}{2}$

Rounding decimals

Round these decimals to the nearest whole number.

3.4 is 3

5.7 is 6

4.5 is 5

If the whole number has .5 after it we write it to the whole number above.

Round these decimals to the nearest whole number.

6.2 is	2.5 is	1.5 is	3.8 is
5.5 is	2.8 is	3.2 is	8.5 is
5.4 is	7.9 is	3.7 is	2.3 is
1.1 is	8.6 is	8.3 is	9.2 is
4.7 is	6.3 is	7.3 is	8.7 is

Round these decimals to the nearest whole number.

14.4 is	42.3 is	74.1 is	59.7 is
29.9 is	32.6 is	63.5 is	96.4 is
18.2 is	37.5 is	39.6 is	76.3 is
40.1 is	28.7 is	26.9 is	12.5 is
29.5 is	38.5 is	87.2 is	41.6 is

Round these decimals to the nearest whole number.

137.6 is	423.5 is	426.2 is	111.8 is
641.6 is	333.5 is	805.2 is	246.8 is
119.5 is	799.6 is	562.3 is	410.2 is
682.4 is	759.6 is	531.5 is	829.9 is
743.4 is	831.1 is	276.7 is	649.3 is

Adding two numbers

Work out the answer to each sum.

```
  271          483
+ 524        + 571
─────        ─────
  795         1054
                 1
```

Remember to carry if you need to.

Work out the answer to each sum.

```
  334          352          723          843
+ 265        + 127        + 345        +1 291
─────        ─────        ─────        ─────
  599          479         1068         2934
```

```
  385          363          535          392
+ 606        + 147        + 187        + 488
─────        ─────        ─────        ─────
```

Write the answer in the box.

213 + 137 =   535 + 167 =

Put the missing number in the box.

```
  3 6 2          2   6          7   1          7 3 9
+ 4 1 9        + 5 8 1        + 2 6 4        + 2 4
───────        ───────        ───────        ───────
  7   1          8 3 7          9 8              7 9
```

Work out the answer to each sum.

One jar contains 204 sweets, another contains 148 sweets. How many sweets are there altogether?

A boy has 136 swap cards, his sister has 159. How many do they have altogether?

Adding two numbers

Work out the answer to each sum.

```
  4 321        3 794
+ 2 465      + 5 325
  6 786        9 119
                 1 1
```

Remember to carry if you need to.

Work out the answer to each sum.

```
  2 642        4 325        2 471
+ 3 241      + 2 653      + 4 238
```

```
  3 749        5 764        8 482
+ 2 471      + 3 915      + 1 349
```

Write the answer in the box.

1 342 + 1 264 =   2 531 + 4 236 =

2 013 + 3 642 =   1 738 + 4 261 =

Put the missing number in the box.

```
    7 4 1          6 5 2          3 6 4 2
+ 2 9 4        + 3 2   4      +     8 3
  6 6 8 4        4 9 2 6        8 4 7 3
```

Work out the answer to each sum.

5 621 people saw the local football team play on Saturday and 3 246 people watched the midweek match. How many people saw the football team play that week?

6 214 people went to the pop concert on Saturday night and 3 471 people went on Sunday night. How many people saw the pop concert that weekend?

Subtracting three-digit numbers

Write the answer in the box.

$$\begin{array}{r} 364 \\ -\ 223 \\ \hline 141 \end{array}$$

$$\begin{array}{r} 4\overset{61}{7}1 \text{ cm} \\ -\ 252 \text{ cm} \\ \hline 219 \text{ cm} \end{array}$$

Write the answer in the box.

$$\begin{array}{r} 263 \\ -\ 151 \\ \hline \end{array}$$

$$\begin{array}{r} 478 \\ -\ 234 \\ \hline \end{array}$$

$$\begin{array}{r} 845 \\ -\ 624 \\ \hline \end{array}$$

$$\begin{array}{r} 793 \\ -\ 581 \\ \hline \end{array}$$

$$\begin{array}{r} 580 \text{ m} \\ -\ 230 \text{ m} \\ \hline \end{array}$$

$$\begin{array}{r} 659 \text{ m} \\ -\ 318 \text{ m} \\ \hline \end{array}$$

$$\begin{array}{r} 850 \text{ m} \\ -\ 740 \text{ m} \\ \hline \end{array}$$

$$\begin{array}{r} 372 \text{ m} \\ -\ 262 \text{ m} \\ \hline \end{array}$$

Write the answer in the box.

365 – 123 =

799 – 354 =

£876 – £515 =

£940 – £730 =

£684 – £574 =

£220 – £120 =

Write the answer in the box.

$$\begin{array}{r} 363 \\ -\ 145 \\ \hline \end{array}$$

$$\begin{array}{r} 484 \\ -\ 237 \\ \hline \end{array}$$

$$\begin{array}{r} 561 \\ -\ 342 \\ \hline \end{array}$$

$$\begin{array}{r} 394 \\ -\ 185 \\ \hline \end{array}$$

$$\begin{array}{r} £937 \\ -\ £719 \\ \hline \end{array}$$

$$\begin{array}{r} £568 \\ -\ £209 \\ \hline \end{array}$$

$$\begin{array}{r} £225 \\ -\ £116 \\ \hline \end{array}$$

$$\begin{array}{r} £752 \\ -\ £329 \\ \hline \end{array}$$

Work out the answer to each sum.

A greengrocer has 234 apples. He sells 127. How many apples does he have left?

A shop has 860 videos to rent. 420 are out on loan. How many are left in the shop?

There are 572 children in a school. 335 are girls. How many are boys?

Subtracting three-digit numbers

Write the answer in the box.

$$
\begin{array}{r}
{}^{3}\!\!\!\!/4^{1}15 \\
-\ 152 \\
\hline
263 \\
\hline
\end{array}
\qquad
\begin{array}{r}
{}^{6}\!\!\!\!/7^{1}1^{0}1\ \text{m} \\
-\ 392\ \text{m} \\
\hline
319\ \text{m} \\
\hline
\end{array}
$$

Write the answer in the box.

$$
\begin{array}{r}
524\ \text{m} \\
-\ 263\ \text{m} \\
\hline
 \\
\hline
\end{array}
\qquad
\begin{array}{r}
319\ \text{m} \\
-\ 137\ \text{m} \\
\hline
 \\
\hline
\end{array}
\qquad
\begin{array}{r}
647\ \text{m} \\
-\ 456\ \text{m} \\
\hline
 \\
\hline
\end{array}
\qquad
\begin{array}{r}
915\ \text{m} \\
-\ 193\ \text{m} \\
\hline
 \\
\hline
\end{array}
$$

$$
\begin{array}{r}
714 \\
-\ 407 \\
\hline
 \\
\hline
\end{array}
\qquad
\begin{array}{r}
926 \\
-\ 827 \\
\hline
 \\
\hline
\end{array}
\qquad
\begin{array}{r}
421 \\
-\ 355 \\
\hline
 \\
\hline
\end{array}
\qquad
\begin{array}{r}
815 \\
-\ 786 \\
\hline
 \\
\hline
\end{array}
$$

Write the answer in the box.

$$512 - 304 = \boxed{} \qquad\qquad 648 - 239 = \boxed{}$$

$$831 - 642 = \boxed{} \qquad\qquad 377 - 198 = \boxed{}$$

Write the answer in the box.

$$
\begin{array}{r}
£423 \\
-\ £136 \\
\hline
 \\
\hline
\end{array}
\qquad
\begin{array}{r}
£615 \\
-\ £418 \\
\hline
 \\
\hline
\end{array}
\qquad
\begin{array}{r}
£312 \\
-\ £113 \\
\hline
 \\
\hline
\end{array}
\qquad
\begin{array}{r}
£924 \\
-\ £528 \\
\hline
 \\
\hline
\end{array}
$$

Write the missing number in the box.

$$
\begin{array}{r}
7\ 2\ 3 \\
-\ 1\ 2\ \boxed{} \\
\hline
5\ 9\ 5 \\
\hline
\end{array}
\qquad
\begin{array}{r}
5\ \boxed{}\ 2 \\
-\ 3\ 1\ 7 \\
\hline
2\ 4\ 5 \\
\hline
\end{array}
\qquad
\begin{array}{r}
8\ 3\ \boxed{} \\
-\ 2\ 5\ 7 \\
\hline
5\ 7\ 7 \\
\hline
\end{array}
\qquad
\begin{array}{r}
5\ 3\ 2 \\
-\ \boxed{}\ \ \ 5 \\
\hline
3\ 4\ 7 \\
\hline
\end{array}
$$

Work out the answer to each sum.

 A cinema holds 645 people. 257 people buy tickets. How many seats are empty?

There are 564 people in a leisure centre. 276 are in the swimming pool. How many are taking part in other activities?

Adding decimal fractions

Write the answer in the box.

£5.25	2.25 m
+ £2.40	+ 3.50 m
£7.65	5.75 m

Write the answer in the box.

£2.25	£7.50	£3.35
+£4.50	+£2.25	+£1.50

£6.45	£3.15	£1.50
+£2.35	+£4.75	+£3.95

5.50 m	3.60 m	7.30 m
+2.35 m	+4.15 m	+1.65 m

6.15 m	3.30 m	5.20 m
+2.20 m	+6.55 m	+1.75 m

Write the answer in the box.

£5.25 + £3.30 =   6.15 m + 1.50 m =   £6.35 + £2.30 =

£5.20 + £2.55 =   2.45 m + 5.10 m =   £7.45 + £1.50 =

Work out the answer to each sum.

A girl has £2.50 pocket money a week. Her brother has £2.75. How much do they have between them?

A boy has 9.50 m of track for his train set. His friend has 7.75 m. If they put their track together, how long would it be?

Answer Section with Parents' Notes

Key Stage 2
Ages 9–10
Workbook 1

This 8-page section provides answers to all the activities in the book. This will enable you to mark your children's work or can be used by them if they prefer to do their own marking.

The notes for each page help explain the common pitfalls and problems and, where appropriate, give indications as to what practice is needed to ensure your children understand where they have gone wrong.

---

2 ☆ Reading and writing numbers

264 346 in words is **Two hundred and sixty-four thousand, three hundred and forty-six**

One million, three hundred and twelve thousand, five hundred and two is **1 312 502**

Write each of these numbers in words.

326 208	Three hundred and twenty-six thousand, two hundred and eight
704 543	Seven hundred and four thousand, five hundred and forty-three
240 701	Two hundred and forty thousand, seven hundred and one
278 520	Two hundred and seventy-eight thousand, five hundred and twenty

Write each of these in numbers.

Five hundred and seventeen thousand and forty-two	517 042
Six hundred and ninety-four thousand, seven hundred and eleven	694 711
Eight hundred and nine thousand, two hundred and three	809 203
Nine hundred thousand, four hundred and four	900 404

Write each of these numbers in words.

9 307 012	Nine million, three hundred and seven thousand and twelve
5 042 390	Five million, forty-two thousand, three hundred and ninety
9 908 434	Nine million, nine hundred and eight thousand, four hundred and thirty-four
8 400 642	Eight million, four hundred thousand, six hundred and forty-two

Write each of these in numbers.

Eight million, two hundred and fifty-one	8 000 251
Two million, forty thousand, four hundred and four	2 040 404
Seven million, three hundred and two thousand, one hundred and one	7 302 101
Two million, five hundred and forty-one thousand and five	2 541 005

Children may miss the significance of zeros and disregard them in their answers. Discuss this confusion with place value carefully. Explain that when writing numbers in words they should not include the zeros in, 'eight thousand, no hundreds and twenty-four'.

---

3 Multiplying and dividing by 10 ☆

Write the answer in the box.
26 x 10 = **260**
42 ÷ 10 = **4 $\frac{2}{10}$**

Write the answer in the box.

76 x 10 = **760**	43 x 10 = **430**	93 x 10 = **930**
66 x 10 = **660**	13 x 10 = **130**	47 x 10 = **470**
147 x 10 = **1 470**	936 x 10 = **9 360**	284 x 10 = **2 840**
364 x 10 = **3 640**	821 x 10 = **8 210**	473 x 10 = **4 730**

Write the answer in the box.

25 ÷ 10 = **2 $\frac{5}{10}$**	17 ÷ 10 = **1 $\frac{7}{10}$**	49 ÷ 10 = **4 $\frac{9}{10}$**
61 ÷ 10 = **6 $\frac{1}{10}$**	33 ÷ 10 = **3 $\frac{3}{10}$**	57 ÷ 10 = **5 $\frac{7}{10}$**
309 ÷ 10 = **30 $\frac{9}{10}$**	247 ÷ 10 = **24 $\frac{7}{10}$**	103 ÷ 10 = **10 $\frac{3}{10}$**
537 ÷ 10 = **53 $\frac{7}{10}$**	893 ÷ 10 = **89 $\frac{3}{10}$**	711 ÷ 10 = **71 $\frac{1}{10}$**

Find the number that has been multiplied by 10.

37 x 10 = 370	**64** x 10 = 640	**74** x 10 = 740
81 x 10 = 810	**10** x 10 = 100	**83** x 10 = 830
714 x 10 = 7 140	**307** x 10 = 3 070	**529** x 10 = 5 290
264 x 10 = 2 640	**829** x 10 = 8 290	**648** x 10 = 6 480

Find the number that has been divided by 10.

39 ÷ 10 = 3 $\frac{9}{10}$	**27** ÷ 10 = 2 $\frac{7}{10}$	**99** ÷ 10 = 9 $\frac{9}{10}$
421 ÷ 10 = 42 $\frac{1}{10}$	**933** ÷ 10 = 93 $\frac{3}{10}$	**747** ÷ 10 = 74 $\frac{7}{10}$
573 ÷ 10 = 57 $\frac{3}{10}$	**381** ÷ 10 = 38 $\frac{1}{10}$	**869** ÷ 10 = 86 $\frac{9}{10}$

Children should realise that multiplying a number by 10 is the same as adding a nought to the original figure. Fractions have been used here but children who understand that $\frac{1}{10}$ is the same as 0.1, may also give answers to the second section as decimals.

---

4 ☆ Ordering sets of large numbers

Write these numbers in order, starting with the smallest.

2 322	526	404	32	1 240	440
32	**404**	**440**	**526**	**1 240**	**2 322**

Write the numbers in each row in order, starting with the smallest.

420	190	950	402	905	986
190	**402**	**420**	**905**	**950**	**986**
308	640	380	805	364	910
308	**364**	**380**	**640**	**805**	**910**
260	350	26	1 000	620	100
26	**100**	**260**	**350**	**620**	**1 000**
20 500	36 820	2 500	45 600	40 560	25 000
2 500	**20 500**	**25 000**	**36 820**	**40 560**	**45 600**

Write the numbers in each row in order, starting with the smallest.

984 000	8 840 000	8 900	98 240	7 560	75 600
7 560	**8 900**	**75 600**	**98 240**	**984 000**	**8 840 000**
301 550	6 405 000	6 450 000	64 500	31 500	3 150
3 150	**31 500**	**64 500**	**301 550**	**6 405 000**	**6 450 000**
7 000 100	70 100	7 100 000	710	710 000	7 100
710	**7 100**	**70 100**	**710 000**	**7 000 100**	**7 100 000**

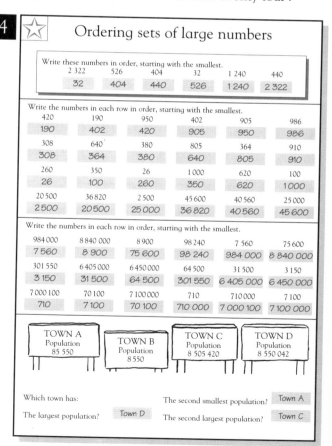

TOWN A Population 85 550
TOWN B Population 8 550
TOWN C Population 8 505 420
TOWN D Population 8 550 042

Which town has:

The largest population? **Town D**

The second smallest population? **Town A**

The second largest population? **Town C**

If children are weak on place value, help them to identify the significant digit when sorting a group of numbers. Explain that, where numbers are close in value, it will be necessary to look to the digits to the right in order to sort.

Rounding numbers

Round these numbers up.
36 to the nearest 10 — 40
124 to the nearest 100 — 100
4 360 to the nearest 1 000 — 4 000
Remember if a number is half-way between it is rounded up.

Write these numbers to the nearest 10.

24 is 20	91 is 90	55 is 60	73 is 70
57 is 60	68 is 70	49 is 50	35 is 40
82 is 80	37 is 40	22 is 20	52 is 50
46 is 50	26 is 30	85 is 90	99 is 100
43 is 40	51 is 50	78 is 80	29 is 30

Write these numbers to the nearest 100.

386 is 400	224 is 200	825 is 800	460 is 500
539 is 500	429 is 400	378 is 400	937 is 900
772 is 800	255 is 300	549 is 500	612 is 600
116 is 100	750 is 800	618 is 600	990 is 1000
940 is 900	843 is 800	172 is 200	868 is 900

Write these numbers to the nearest 1 000.

3 240 is 3 000	2 500 is 3 000	9 940 is 10 000	1 051 is 1 000
8 945 is 9 000	5 050 is 5 000	5 530 is 6 000	4 850 is 5 000
6 200 is 6 000	7 250 is 7 000	8 499 is 8 000	8 450 is 8 000
12 501 is 13 000	8 762 is 9 000	6 500 is 7 000	3 292 is 3 000
1 499 is 1 000	14 836 is 15 000	10 650 is 11 000	11 241 is 11 000

Rounding a number means making it closest to the specified amount. Use of a number line may be necessary, especially for some sections. If necessary, remind children that for 5 or 50 or 500 the convention is to round up.

Counting on in constant steps

Continue each row.

Steps of 9:	5	14	23	32	41	50
Steps of 14:	20	34	48	62	76	90

Continue each row.

21	38	55	72	89	106	123	140
13	37	61	85	109	133	157	181
7	25	43	61	79	97	115	133
32	48	64	80	96	112	128	144
12	31	50	69	88	107	126	145
32	54	76	98	120	142	164	186
24	64	104	144	184	224	264	304
4	34	64	94	124	154	184	214
36	126	216	306	396	486	576	666
12	72	132	192	252	312	372	432
25	45	65	85	105	125	145	165
22	72	122	172	222	272	322	372
25	100	175	250	325	400	475	550
60	165	270	375	480	585	690	795
8	107	206	305	404	503	602	701
10	61	112	163	214	265	316	367
26	127	228	329	430	531	632	733
48	100	152	204	256	308	360	412

This is fairly simple once children realise that the steps involved can be found by taking the first number away from the second, or the second from the third as a double check. They should identify 'difference' with subtraction.

Recognising multiples of 6, 7, and 8

Circle the multiples of 6.
8 (12) 15 (18) 20 (24)

Circle the multiples of 6.

8	22	14	(18)	(36)	40
16	38	44	25	(30)	(60)
(6)	21	19	(54)	56	(24)
(12)	(48)	10	20	35	26
(42)	39	23	28	(36)	32

Circle the multiples of 7.

(7)	17	24	59	(42)	55
15	20	(21)	46	12	(70)
(14)	27	69	36	47	(49)
65	19	57	(28)	38	(63)
33	34	(35)	37	60	(56)

Circle the multiples of 8.

(40)	26	15	25	38	(56)
26	(8)	73	41	(64)	12
75	58	62	(24)	31	(72)
12	(80)	(32)	46	38	78
(16)	42	66	28	(48)	68

Circle the number that is a multiple of 6 and 7.
18 54 (42) 21 28 63

Circle the numbers that are multiples of 6 and 8.
16 (24) 36 (48) 54 42

Circle the number that is a multiple of 7 and 8.
24 32 40 28 42 (56)

Success on this page will basically depend on a knowledge of multiplication tables. Where children experience difficulty, multiplication table practice should be encouraged.

Factors of numbers from 1 to 30

The factors of 10 are 1 2 5 10
Circle the factors of 4 (1) (2) 3 (4)

Write all the factors of these numbers.

The factors of 26 are	1, 2, 13, 26
The factors of 30 are	1, 2, 3, 5, 6, 10, 15, 30
The factors of 9 are	1, 3, 9
The factors of 12 are	1, 2, 3, 4, 6, 12
The factors of 15 are	1, 3, 5, 15
The factors of 22 are	1, 2, 11, 22
The factors of 20 are	1, 2, 4, 5, 10, 20
The factors of 21 are	1, 3, 7, 21
The factors of 24 are	1, 2, 3, 4, 6, 8, 12, 24

Circle all the factors of these numbers.

Which numbers are factors of 14? (1)(2) 3 5 (7) 9 12 (14)
Which numbers are factors of 13? (1) 2 3 4 5 6 7 8 9 10 11 (13)
Which numbers are factors of 7? (1) 2 3 4 5 6 (7)
Which numbers are factors of 11? (1) 2 3 4 5 6 7 8 9 10 (11)
Which numbers are factors of 6? (1)(2)(3) 4 5 (6)
Which numbers are factors of 8? (1)(2) 3 (4) 5 6 7 (8)
Which numbers are factors of 17? (1) 2 5 7 12 14 16 (17)
Which numbers are factors of 18? (1)(2)(3) 4 5 (6) 8 (9) 10 12 (18)

Some numbers only have factors of 1 and themselves. They are called prime numbers. Write down all the prime numbers that are less than 30 in the box.

2, 3, 5, 7, 11, 13, 17, 19, 23, 29

Encourage a systematic approach such as starting 1 and working forward to the number that is half o the number in question. Children often forget that and itself are factors of a number. You may need t point out that 1 is not a prime number.

Recognising equivalent fractions ☆

Make these fractions equal by putting a number in the box.

$$\frac{1}{2} = \frac{2}{4} \qquad \frac{1}{3} = \frac{2}{6}$$

Make these fractions equal by putting a number in the box.

$\frac{1}{2} = \frac{5}{10}$	$\frac{3}{4} = \frac{6}{8}$	$\frac{1}{3} = \frac{3}{9}$
$\frac{2}{3} = \frac{8}{12}$	$\frac{6}{12} = \frac{3}{6}$	$\frac{4}{8} = \frac{1}{2}$
$\frac{1}{5} = \frac{2}{10}$	$\frac{4}{12} = \frac{2}{6}$	$\frac{3}{5} = \frac{6}{10}$
$\frac{1}{4} = \frac{2}{8}$	$\frac{6}{18} = \frac{1}{3}$	$\frac{3}{12} = \frac{1}{4}$
$\frac{3}{9} = \frac{1}{3}$	$\frac{4}{10} = \frac{2}{5}$	$\frac{3}{4} = \frac{9}{12}$
$\frac{4}{16} = \frac{1}{4}$	$\frac{15}{20} = \frac{3}{4}$	$\frac{6}{12} = \frac{1}{2}$
$\frac{3}{5} = \frac{6}{10}$	$\frac{3}{6} = \frac{1}{2}$	$\frac{9}{12} = \frac{3}{4}$

Make these rows of fractions equal by putting a number in each box.

$\frac{1}{2}$ =	$\frac{2}{4}$ =	$\frac{3}{6}$ =	$\frac{4}{8}$ =	$\frac{5}{10}$ =	$\frac{6}{12}$
$\frac{1}{4}$ =	$\frac{2}{8}$ =	$\frac{3}{12}$ =	$\frac{4}{16}$ =	$\frac{5}{20}$ =	$\frac{6}{24}$
$\frac{3}{4}$ =	$\frac{6}{8}$ =	$\frac{9}{12}$ =	$\frac{12}{16}$ =	$\frac{15}{20}$ =	$\frac{18}{24}$
$\frac{1}{3}$ =	$\frac{2}{6}$ =	$\frac{3}{9}$ =	$\frac{4}{12}$ =	$\frac{5}{15}$ =	$\frac{12}{36}$
$\frac{1}{5}$ =	$\frac{2}{10}$ =	$\frac{3}{15}$ =	$\frac{4}{20}$ =	$\frac{5}{25}$ =	$\frac{6}{30}$
$\frac{2}{3}$ =	$\frac{4}{6}$ =	$\frac{6}{9}$ =	$\frac{8}{12}$ =	$\frac{10}{15}$ =	$\frac{14}{21}$

If the children have problems with this page, point out that fractions remain the same as long as you multiply or divide the numerator and denominator by the same number.

Ordering sets of simple fractions

Put these numbers in order starting with the smallest.

2	$1\frac{1}{2}$	$\frac{1}{2}$	$\frac{1}{4}$	$1\frac{3}{4}$
$\frac{1}{4}$	$\frac{1}{2}$	$1\frac{1}{2}$	$1\frac{3}{4}$	2

Put these numbers in order starting with the smallest.

4	$2\frac{1}{2}$	$1\frac{3}{4}$	$1\frac{1}{4}$	$3\frac{1}{2}$	$1\frac{1}{4}$	$1\frac{3}{4}$	$2\frac{1}{2}$	$3\frac{1}{2}$	4
2	$1\frac{1}{2}$	1	$2\frac{1}{4}$	3	1	$1\frac{1}{2}$	2	$2\frac{1}{4}$	3
2	$1\frac{1}{4}$	$3\frac{1}{2}$	$1\frac{1}{2}$	$2\frac{1}{2}$	$1\frac{1}{4}$	$1\frac{1}{2}$	2	$2\frac{1}{2}$	$3\frac{1}{2}$
$7\frac{1}{2}$	$3\frac{1}{4}$	$1\frac{1}{2}$	$1\frac{1}{4}$	$2\frac{3}{4}$	$1\frac{1}{4}$	$1\frac{1}{2}$	$2\frac{3}{4}$	$3\frac{1}{4}$	$7\frac{1}{2}$
$4\frac{1}{4}$	$3\frac{1}{2}$	$2\frac{3}{4}$	$2\frac{1}{2}$	$3\frac{1}{4}$	$2\frac{1}{2}$	$2\frac{3}{4}$	$3\frac{1}{4}$	$3\frac{1}{2}$	$4\frac{1}{4}$
$3\frac{3}{4}$	$3\frac{1}{3}$	$4\frac{1}{4}$	$3\frac{2}{3}$	$3\frac{1}{2}$	$3\frac{1}{3}$	$3\frac{1}{2}$	$3\frac{2}{3}$	$3\frac{3}{4}$	$4\frac{1}{4}$
$4\frac{2}{3}$	$4\frac{1}{2}$	$4\frac{3}{4}$	$4\frac{1}{3}$	$5\frac{1}{4}$	$4\frac{1}{3}$	$4\frac{1}{2}$	$4\frac{2}{3}$	$4\frac{3}{4}$	$5\frac{1}{4}$
$7\frac{1}{2}$	$6\frac{2}{3}$	$7\frac{3}{4}$	$7\frac{1}{4}$	$6\frac{1}{2}$	$6\frac{1}{2}$	$6\frac{2}{3}$	$7\frac{1}{4}$	$7\frac{1}{2}$	$7\frac{3}{4}$
$14\frac{1}{2}$	$15\frac{3}{4}$	$15\frac{1}{2}$	$14\frac{3}{4}$	$13\frac{3}{4}$	$13\frac{3}{4}$	$14\frac{1}{2}$	$14\frac{3}{4}$	$15\frac{1}{2}$	$15\frac{3}{4}$
$7\frac{1}{3}$	$8\frac{1}{2}$	$7\frac{3}{4}$	$8\frac{1}{5}$	$7\frac{2}{3}$	$7\frac{1}{3}$	$7\frac{2}{3}$	$7\frac{3}{4}$	$8\frac{1}{5}$	$8\frac{1}{2}$
$10\frac{1}{5}$	$9\frac{3}{4}$	$10\frac{1}{2}$	$9\frac{1}{5}$	$9\frac{1}{2}$	$9\frac{1}{5}$	$9\frac{1}{2}$	$9\frac{3}{4}$	$10\frac{1}{5}$	$10\frac{1}{2}$

The most likely area of difficulty will be sorting fractions such as $\frac{3}{4}$ and $\frac{2}{3}$ or $\frac{1}{3}$ and $\frac{1}{4}$. If children experience difficulty, refer back to the previous page or, using two pieces of card, cut one into quarters and one into thirds to allow comparison.

Rounding decimals ☆

Round these decimals to the nearest whole number.

3.4 is	3	
5.7 is	6	
4.5 is	5	

If the whole number has .5 after it, we round it to the whole number above.

Round these decimals to the nearest whole number.

6.2 is 6	2.5 is 3	1.5 is 2	3.8 is 4
5.5 is 6	2.8 is 3	3.2 is 3	8.5 is 9
5.4 is 5	7.9 is 8	3.7 is 4	2.3 is 2
1.1 is 1	8.6 is 9	8.3 is 8	9.2 is 9
4.7 is 5	6.3 is 6	7.3 is 7	8.7 is 9

Round these decimals to the nearest whole number.

14.4 is 14	42.3 is 42	74.1 is 74	59.7 is 60
29.9 is 30	32.6 is 33	63.5 is 64	96.4 is 96
18.2 is 18	37.5 is 38	39.6 is 40	76.3 is 76
40.1 is 40	28.7 is 29	26.9 is 27	12.5 is 13
29.5 is 30	38.5 is 39	87.2 is 87	41.6 is 42

Round these decimals to the nearest whole number.

137.6 is 138	423.5 is 424	426.2 is 426	111.8 is 112
641.6 is 642	333.5 is 334	805.2 is 805	246.8 is 247
119.5 is 120	799.6 is 800	562.3 is 562	410.2 is 410
682.4 is 682	759.6 is 760	531.5 is 532	829.9 is 830
743.4 is 743	831.1 is 831	276.7 is 277	649.3 is 649

If children experience difficulty, point out the similarity to the work done on page 5. Use of a number line showing tenths can help. A likely error will be when a number with 9 in the units digit is rounded up. Children also often forget to alter the tens digit.

Adding two numbers

Work out the answer to each sum,

```
  271        483
+ 524      + 571
─────      ──────
  795       1054
```

Remember to carry if you need to.

Work out the answer to each sum.

```
  334        352        723        843
+ 265      + 127      + 345      + 291
─────      ─────      ──────     ──────
  599        479       1068       1134

  385        363        535        392
+ 606      + 147      + 187      + 488
─────      ─────      ─────      ─────
  991        510        722        880
```

Write the answer in the box.

213 + 137 = 350   535 + 167 = 702

Put the missing number in the box.

```
  3 6 2      2 5 6      7 2 1      7 3 9
+ 4 1 9    + 5 8 1    + 2 6 4    + 2 4 0
───────    ───────    ───────    ───────
  7 8 1      8 3 7      9 8 5      9 7 9
```

Work out the answer to each sum.

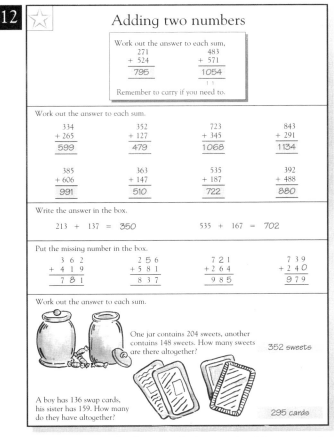

One jar contains 204 sweets, another contains 148 sweets. How many sweets are there altogether?   352 sweets

A boy has 136 swap cards, his sister has 159. How many do they have altogether?   295 cards

This page has fairly straightforward addition work, with some horizontal sums. Children should be able to work horizontally as well as vertically. Most likely errors will be in forgetting to carry.

13 — Adding two numbers

Work out the answer to each sum.
```
  4 321          3 794
+ 2 465        + 5 325
  6 786          9 119
                   1 1
```
Remember to carry if you need to.

Work out the answer to each sum.
```
  2 642          4 325          2 471
+ 3 241        + 2 653        + 4 238
  5 883          6 978          6 709
                                  1

  3 749          5 764          8 482
+ 2 471        + 3 915        + 1 349
  6 220          9 679          9 831
```

Write the answer in the box.

1 342 + 1 264 = 2 606   2 531 + 4 236 = 6 767

2 013 + 3 642 = 5 655   1 738 + 4 261 = 5 999

Put the missing number in the box.
```
  3 7 4 1        1 6 5 2        3 6 4 2
+ 2 9 4 3      + 3 2 7 4      + 4 8 3 1
  6 6 8 4        4 9 2 6        8 4 7 3
```

Work out the answer to each sum.

5 621 people saw the local football team play on Saturday and 3 246 people watched the midweek match. How many people saw the football team play that week?   **8 867 people**

6 214 people went to the pop concert on Saturday night and 3 471 people went on Sunday night. How many people saw the pop concert that weekend?   **9 685 people**

Similar to the previous page but with slightly larger numbers. Ensure that children carry when necessary.

14 — Subtracting three-digit numbers

Write the answer in the box.
```
  364           4⁶¹1 cm
- 223          - 252 cm
  141            219 cm
```

Write the answer in the box.
```
  263      478      845      793
- 151    - 234    - 624    - 581
  112      244      221      212

  580 m    659 m    850 m    372 m
- 230 m  - 318 m  - 740 m  - 262 m
  350 m    341 m    110 m    110 m
```

Write the answer in the box.

365 − 123 = 242   799 − 354 = 445

£876 − £515 = £361   £940 − £730 = £210

£684 − £574 = £110   £220 − £120 = £100

Write the answer in the box.
```
  3⁵¹3    4⁷¹4    5⁵¹1    3⁸¹4
- 145    - 237    - 342    - 185
  218      247      219      209

  £9³¹7   £5⁶¹8   £2²¹5   £7⁴¹2
- £719   - £209   - £116   - £329
  £218    £359     £109     £423
```

Work out the answer to each sum.

A greengrocer has 234 apples. He sells 127. How many apples does he have left?   **107 apples**

A shop has 860 videos to rent. 420 are out on loan. How many are left in the shop?   **440 videos**

There are 572 children in a school. 335 are girls. How many are boys?   **237 boys**

In some of these sums, a common error is for children to take the smallest number from the largest, irrespective of whether the smaller number is on the top or the bottom. They should be able to 'borrow' or 'steal' from the digit on the left.

15 — Subtracting three-digit numbers

Write the answer in the box.
```
  ⁴¹⁵15         ⁶⁰¹711 m
- 152          - 392 m
  263            319 m
```

Write the answer in the box.
```
  ⁴¹324 m   ²319 m   ⁵¹647 m   ⁸¹915 m
- 263 m   - 137 m   - 456 m   - 193 m
  261 m     182 m     191 m     722 m

  ⁶¹714    ⁹926    ⁴¹¹421   ⁷⁶¹815
- 407    - 827    - 355    - 786
  307      99       66       29
```

Write the answer in the box.

512 − 304 = 208   648 − 239 = 409

831 − 642 = 189   377 − 198 = 179

Write the answer in the box.
```
  £⁴¹423   £⁵¹⁰¹615   £⁴³¹₂    £⁸¹924
- £136    - £418    - £113    - £528
  £287     £197      £199      £396
```

Write the missing number in the box.
```
  7 2 3     5 6 2     8 3 4     5 3 2
- 1 2 8   - 3 1 7   - 2 5 7   - 1 8 5
  5 9 5     2 4 5     5 7 7     3 4 7
```

Work out the answer to each sum.

A cinema holds 645 people. 257 people buy tickets. How many seats are empty?   **388 seats**

There are 564 people in a leisure centre. 276 are in the swimming pool. How many are taking part in other activities?   **288 people**

The work on this page is similar to the previous page but decomposition is also required for the tens digits to be taken away. This means 'borrowing' or 'stealing' from the left. It is better to use the term 'stealing' since the number taken is never returned.

16 — Adding decimal fractions

Write the answer in the box..
```
  £5.25           2.25 m
+ £2.40         + 3.50 m
  £7.65           5.75 m
```

Write the answer in the box.
```
  £2.25      £7.50      £3.35
+ £4.50    + £2.25    + £1.50
  £6.75      £9.75      £4.85

  £6.45      £3.15      £1.50
+ £2.35    + £4.75    + £3.95
  £8.80      £7.90      £5.45

  5.50 m     3.60 m     7.30 m
+ 2.35 m   + 4.15 m   + 1.65 m
  7.85 m     7.75 m     8.95 m

  6.15 m     3.30 m     5.20 m
+ 2.20 m   + 6.55 m   + 1.75 m
  8.35 m     9.85 m     6.95 m
```

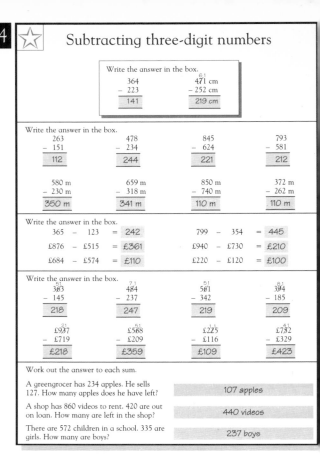

Write the answer in the box.

£5.25 + £3.30 = £8.55   6.15 m + 1.50 m = 7.65 m   £6.35 + £2.30 = £8.65

£5.20 + £2.55 = £7.75   2.45 m + 5.10 m = 7.55 m   £7.45 + £1.50 = £8.95

Work out the answer to each sum.

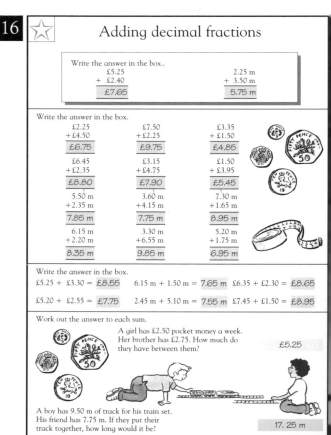

A girl has £2.50 pocket money a week. Her brother has £2.75. How much do they have between them?   **£5.25**

A boy has 9.50 m of track for his train set. His friend has 7.75 m. If they put their track together, how long would it be?   **17. 25 m**

This page should proceed straightforwardly from the earlier addition work, but children may need to be reminded to place the decimal point correctly in the answer, particularly when doing horizontal sums. Reminders to carry may also be necessary.

Adding decimal fractions

Write the answer in the box.

£3.35 + £5.55 **£8.90**	3.45 m + 1.25 m **4.70 m**

Write the answer in the box.

£3.60 + £2.25 **£5.85**	£1.25 + £4.55 **£5.80**	£7.45 + £2.35 **£9.80**
£3.60 + £3.25 **£6.85**	£7.35 + £1.45 **£8.80**	£5.25 + £2.65 **£7.90**
3.45 m + 4.35 m **7.80 m**	8.55 m + 1.35 m **9.90 m**	1.75 m + 5.20 m **6.95 m**
2.40 m + 1.45 m **3.85 m**	7.15 m + 1.35 m **8.50 m**	3.85 m + 4.10 m **7.95 m**

Write the answer in the box.

£2.75 + £4.15 = **£6.90**   3.75 m + 2.75 m = **6.50 m**   £3.65 + £1.50 = **£5.15**

£6.25 + £1.50 = **£7.75**   8.65 m + 2.55 m = **11.20 m** £3.45 + £1.55 = **£5.00**

Work out the answer to each sum.

George buys two magazines that cost £2.55 and £1.75. How much does he spend?   **£4.30**

Jennifer buys two rolls of sticky tape. One contains 7.75 m and the other contains 6.75 m. How much tape does she have altogether?   **14.5 m**

When adding metres, the second decimal place is given even when it is nought. The last answer leaves off the nought to provide an opportunity through discussion to show the children that the second nought is not necessary.

Subtracting decimal fractions

Write the answer in the box.

£6.55 – £3.20 **£3.35**	4.70 m – 2.50 m **2.20 m**

Write the answer in the box.

£7.45 – £3.30 **£4.15**	£9.60 – £7.20 **£2.40**	£5.55 – £2.40 **£3.15**
£8.35 – £3.25 **£5.10**	£3.95 – £1.75 **£2.20**	£6.55 – £2.40 **£4.15**

Write the answer in the box.

3.90 m – 1.40 m **2.50 m**	4.75 m – 3.35 m **1.40 m**	9.20 m – 2.20 m **7.00 m**
7.55 m – 1.15 m **6.40 m**	2.15 m – 1.00 m **1.15 m**	3.35 m – 2.20 m **1.15 m**

Write the answer in the box.

£4.15 – £1.10 = **£3.05**   £3.55 – £2.50 = **£1.05**

£9.75 – £4.30 = **£5.45**   £8.85 – £6.05 = **£2.80**

7.55 m – 2.30 m = **5.25 m**   6.15 m – 4.05 m = **2.10 m**

Work out the answer to each sum.

Khaleda has £4.65 to spend. She buys a book for £3.45. How much does she have left?   **£1.20**

Eoin is given £9.50 for his birthday. If he spends £3.20 at the cinema how much will he have left?   **£6.30**

This should follow on from the previous subtraction work. If children are unsure, explain that once the decimal point is placed in the answer box the sum can be done as conventional subtraction.

Subtracting decimal fractions

Write the answer in the box.

£3.35 – £2.40 **£2.95**	7.35 m – 1.65 m **5.70 m**

Write the answer in the box.

£6.55 – £2.75 **£3.80**	£7.45 – £3.65 **£3.80**	£8.65 – £4.75 **£3.90**
£3.15 – £1.25 **£1.90**	£5.70 – £2.90 **£2.80**	£4.15 – £1.75 **£2.40**

Write the answer in the box.

5.35 m – 2.55 m **2.80 m**	7.25 m – 2.55 m **4.70 m**	4.15 m – 2.25 m **1.90 m**
5.45 m – 2.55 m **2.90 m**	8.15 m – 2.20 m **5.95 m**	7.30 m – 3.50 m **3.80**

Write the answer in the box.

£6.25 – £2.50 = **£3.75**   £4.35 – £2.55 = **£1.80**

£5.20 – £3.30 = **£1.90**   £7.40 – £3.80 = **£3.60**

6.45 m – 2.55 m = **3.90 m**   7.35 m – 3.55 m = **3.80 m**

Work out the answer to each sum.

Kevin has a piece of wood 4.55 m long. He cuts off a piece 1.65 m long. How much does he have left?   **2.90 m**

Abir's long jump result is 2.35 m. Steven's is 1.40 m. How much longer is Abir's jump than Steven's?   **0.95 m**

This follows on from page 18, but involves decomposition. If children are unsure about stealing across the decimal point, reassure them that this is acceptable and should be dealt with in the same way as a conventional subtraction using decomposition.

Multiplying by units

Complete these sums.

32 x 2 **64**	26 x 3 **78**	34 x 4 **136**

Complete these sums.

27 x 2 **54**	32 x 3 **96**	16 x 4 **64**	19 x 2 **38**
22 x 3 **66**	25 x 4 **100**	18 x 6 **108**	33 x 5 **165**
39 x 2 **78**	26 x 2 **52**	41 x 2 **82**	38 x 3 **114**
29 x 3 **87**	45 x 2 **90**	28 x 3 **84**	16 x 6 **96**
10 x 5 **50**	40 x 2 **80**	20 x 4 **80**	50 x 3 **150**

Work out the answer to each sum.

Laura has 36 marbles but Sarah has twice as many. How many marbles does Sarah have?   **72 marbles**

A ruler is 30 centimetres long. How long will 4 rulers be?   **120 cm**

Ensure that children understand the convention of multiplication sums, i.e. multiply units first and work left. Problems here will generally highlight gaps in their knowledge of multiplication tables 2, 3, 4, and 5. One other possible error could be a failure to carry.

Multiplying by units

Complete these sums.

$$\begin{array}{c} 53 \\ \times\ 3 \\ \hline 159 \end{array} \qquad \begin{array}{c} 76 \\ \times\ 6 \\ \hline 456 \end{array} \qquad \begin{array}{c} 25 \\ \times\ 7 \\ \hline 175 \end{array}$$

Complete these sums.

$$\begin{array}{c} 56 \\ \times\ 8 \\ \hline 448 \end{array} \qquad \begin{array}{c} 46 \\ \times\ 7 \\ \hline 322 \end{array} \qquad \begin{array}{c} 32 \\ \times\ 6 \\ \hline 192 \end{array} \qquad \begin{array}{c} 36 \\ \times\ 9 \\ \hline 324 \end{array}$$

$$\begin{array}{c} 45 \\ \times\ 4 \\ \hline 180 \end{array} \qquad \begin{array}{c} 73 \\ \times\ 5 \\ \hline 365 \end{array} \qquad \begin{array}{c} 96 \\ \times\ 3 \\ \hline 288 \end{array} \qquad \begin{array}{c} 58 \\ \times\ 7 \\ \hline 406 \end{array}$$

$$\begin{array}{c} 33 \\ \times\ 6 \\ \hline 198 \end{array} \quad \begin{array}{c} 48 \\ \times\ 5 \\ \hline 240 \end{array} \quad \begin{array}{c} 24 \\ \times\ 9 \\ \hline 216 \end{array} \quad \begin{array}{c} 19 \\ \times\ 8 \\ \hline 152 \end{array} \quad \begin{array}{c} 64 \\ \times\ 4 \\ \hline 256 \end{array} \quad \begin{array}{c} 52 \\ \times\ 6 \\ \hline 312 \end{array}$$

$$\begin{array}{c} 81 \\ \times\ 3 \\ \hline 243 \end{array} \quad \begin{array}{c} 37 \\ \times\ 7 \\ \hline 259 \end{array} \quad \begin{array}{c} 40 \\ \times\ 8 \\ \hline 320 \end{array} \quad \begin{array}{c} 50 \\ \times\ 3 \\ \hline 150 \end{array} \quad \begin{array}{c} 30 \\ \times\ 7 \\ \hline 210 \end{array} \quad \begin{array}{c} 20 \\ \times\ 9 \\ \hline 180 \end{array}$$

Work out the answer to each sum.

A school coach holds 36 children. How many children can you get in 6 coach loads? — 216 children

28 children bring 7 comics each to school. How many comics do they have altogether? — 196 comics

As on the previous page, problems here will generally highlight gaps in children's knowledge of the 6, 7, 8, and 9 multiplication tables. As before, the other most likely error to occur will be a failure to carry.

Division with fraction remainders

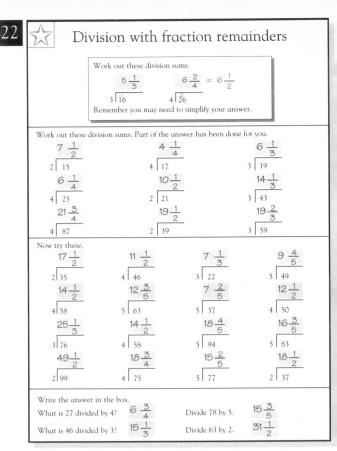

Work out these division sums.

$$5\frac{1}{3} \qquad 6\frac{2}{4} = 6\frac{1}{2}$$
$$3\overline{)16} \qquad 4\overline{)26}$$

Remember you may need to simplify your answer.

Work out these division sums. Part of the answer has been done for you.

$$7\frac{1}{2} \quad 2\overline{)15} \qquad 4\frac{1}{4} \quad 4\overline{)17} \qquad 6\frac{1}{3} \quad 3\overline{)19}$$

$$6\frac{1}{4} \quad 4\overline{)25} \qquad 10\frac{1}{2} \quad 2\overline{)21} \qquad 14\frac{1}{3} \quad 3\overline{)43}$$

$$21\frac{3}{4} \quad 4\overline{)87} \qquad 19\frac{1}{2} \quad 2\overline{)39} \qquad 19\frac{2}{3} \quad 3\overline{)59}$$

Now try these.

$$17\frac{1}{2} \quad 2\overline{)35} \qquad 11\frac{1}{2} \quad 4\overline{)46} \qquad 7\frac{1}{3} \quad 3\overline{)22} \qquad 9\frac{4}{5} \quad 5\overline{)49}$$

$$14\frac{1}{2} \quad 4\overline{)58} \qquad 12\frac{3}{5} \quad 5\overline{)63} \qquad 7\frac{2}{5} \quad 5\overline{)37} \qquad 12\frac{1}{2} \quad 4\overline{)50}$$

$$25\frac{1}{3} \quad 3\overline{)76} \qquad 14\frac{1}{2} \quad 4\overline{)58} \qquad 18\frac{4}{5} \quad 5\overline{)94} \qquad 16\frac{3}{5} \quad 5\overline{)83}$$

$$49\frac{1}{2} \quad 2\overline{)99} \qquad 18\frac{3}{4} \quad 4\overline{)75} \qquad 15\frac{2}{5} \quad 5\overline{)77} \qquad 18\frac{1}{2} \quad 2\overline{)37}$$

Write the answer in the box.

What is 27 divided by 4? $6\frac{3}{4}$ Divide 78 by 5. $15\frac{3}{5}$

What is 46 divided by 3? $15\frac{1}{3}$ Divide 63 by 2. $31\frac{1}{2}$

Most children will be familiar with remainders. If they are unsure of how to get to a fraction, discuss with them the relationship between the remainder and the divider and the fractional answer. Gaps in their knowledge of multiplication tables 2 to 5 may be apparent.

Division with fraction remainders

Work out these division sums.

$$5\frac{4}{6} = 5\frac{2}{3} \qquad 7\frac{1}{7}$$
$$6\overline{)34} \qquad 7\overline{)50}$$

Remember you may need to simplify your answer.

Work out these division sums. Part of the answer has been done for you.

$$12\frac{1}{6} \quad 6\overline{)73} \qquad 11\frac{4}{7} \quad 7\overline{)81} \qquad 11\frac{5}{8} \quad 8\overline{)93}$$

$$10\frac{2}{9} \quad 9\overline{)92} \qquad 8\frac{1}{8} \quad 8\overline{)65} \qquad 12\frac{6}{7} \quad 7\overline{)90}$$

$$5\frac{2}{9} \quad 9\overline{)47} \qquad 5\frac{1}{7} \quad 7\overline{)36} \qquad 13\frac{5}{6} \quad 6\overline{)83}$$

Now try these.

$$16\frac{1}{2} \quad 6\overline{)99} \qquad 7\frac{1}{6} \quad 6\overline{)43} \qquad 3\frac{1}{3} \quad 9\overline{)30} \qquad 9\frac{1}{2} \quad 8\overline{)76}$$

$$7\frac{3}{7} \quad 7\overline{)52} \qquad 11\frac{6}{7} \quad 7\overline{)83} \qquad 5\frac{7}{9} \quad 9\overline{)52} \qquad 15\frac{1}{6} \quad 6\overline{)91}$$

$$9\frac{3}{7} \quad 7\overline{)66} \qquad 7\frac{7}{8} \quad 8\overline{)63} \qquad 4\frac{1}{2} \quad 6\overline{)27} \qquad 5\frac{3}{4} \quad 8\overline{)46}$$

$$10\frac{1}{3} \quad 9\overline{)93} \qquad 12\frac{1}{7} \quad 7\overline{)85} \qquad 8\frac{3}{8} \quad 8\overline{)67} \qquad 3\frac{5}{7} \quad 7\overline{)26}$$

Write the answer in the box.

What is 85 divided by 7? $12\frac{1}{7}$ Divide 84 by 8. $10\frac{1}{2}$

What is 75 divided by 6? $12\frac{1}{2}$ Divide 73 by 9. $8\frac{1}{9}$

The notes from the previous page apply here, but the multiplication tables used are 6, 7, 8, and 9.

Real life problems

Write the answer in the box.

Yasmin has £4.60 and she is given another £1.20. How much does she have?

£5.80

$$\begin{array}{r} £4.60 \\ +\ £1.20 \\ \hline £5.80 \end{array}$$

David has 12 packets of sweets. He gives them to his 5 friends. How many packets do they each get? $2\frac{2}{5}$

$$2\frac{2}{5} \qquad 5\overline{)12}$$

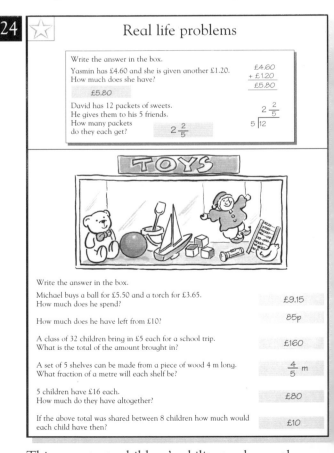

Write the answer in the box.

Michael buys a ball for £5.50 and a torch for £3.65. How much does he spend? — £9.15

How much does he have left from £10? — 85p

A class of 32 children bring in £5 each for a school trip. What is the total of the amount brought in? — £160

A set of 5 shelves can be made from a piece of wood 4 m long. What fraction of a metre will each shelf be? — $\frac{4}{5}$ m

5 children have £16 each. How much do they have altogether? — £80

If the above total was shared between 8 children how much would each child have then? — £10

This page tests children's ability to choose the operation required to solve real life problems, mostly involving money. Discussing whether the answer will be larger or smaller than the question will help children decide on their choice of operation.

Real life problems

Work out the answer to each sum.

A box is 16 cm wide. How wide will 6 boxes be if placed together?
96 cm

```
  16 cm
 ×  6
  96 cm
     3
```

Josh is 1.20 m tall. His sister is 1.55 m tall. How much taller than Josh is his sister?

0.35 m

```
  1.55 m
 −1.20 m
  0.35 m
```

Work out the answer to each sum.

A tin contains 56 g of gravy powder. If 12 g are used, how much is left?
44g

```
  56 g
 − 12 g
  44 g
```

A large jar of coffee weighs 280 g. A smaller jar weighs 130 g. How much heavier is the larger jar than the smaller jar?
150g

```
  280 g
 − 130 g
  150 g
```

There are 7 shelves of books. 5 shelves are 1.2 m long. 2 shelves are 1.5 m long. What is the total length of the 7 shelves?
9 m

```
  1.2      1.5
 × 5      × 2
  6.0      3.0

  6 + 3 = 9
```

A pop star can sign 36 photographs in a minute. How many can he sign in 30 seconds?
18

```
    18
 2 ⟌ 36
```

Natalie has read 5 pages of a 20-page comic. If it has taken her 9 minutes, how long is it likely to take her to read the whole comic?
36 minutes

```
   1.8        2.0
 5 ⟌ 9.0    × 1.8
              16.0
              20.0
              36
```

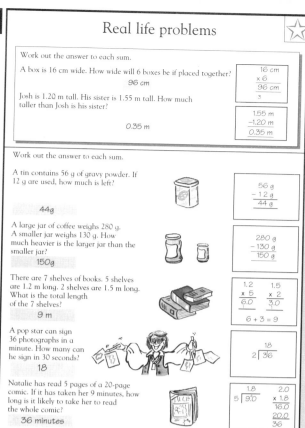

This page continues the real life problems but with units other than money. Note that in the 3rd question there are three operations required to arrive at the answer.

Area of rectangles and squares

Find the area of this rectangle.

15   cm²

5 cm / 3 cm

To find the area of a rectangle or square we multiply length (l) by width (w).
Area = l × w = 5 cm × 3 cm = 15 cm²

Find the area of these rectangles and squares.

2 cm / 5 cm — 10 cm²

4 cm / 4 cm — 16 cm²

3 cm / 8 cm — 24 cm²

2 cm / 2 cm — 4 cm²

7 cm / 2 cm — 14 cm²

3 cm / 9 cm — 27 cm²

6 cm / 4 cm — 24 cm²

5 cm / 4 cm — 20 cm²

5 cm / 5 cm — 25 cm²

Children multiply the two sides together to arrive at the area. It would be worthwhile discussing the concept of square units (cm²) with the child. If the answers are wrong ensure that children are not adding the sides instead of multiplying.

Word problems with time

Work out the answer to this sum.

A train leaves the station at 7.30 a.m. and arrives at the end of the line at 10.45 a.m. How long did the journey take?
3 hours 15 minutes

```
  10.45
 − 7.30
   3.15
```

Work out the answer to each sum.

A film starts at 7.00 p.m. and finishes at 8.45 p.m. How long is the film?
1 hour 45 minutes

```
   8.45
 − 7.00
   1.45
```

A cake takes 2 hours 25 minutes to cook. If it needs to be ready by 4.00 p.m., what time does it need to be put in the oven?
1.35 p.m.

```
  3.60
  4.00
 − 2.25
  1.35
```

Sanjay needs to clean his bedroom and wash the car. It takes him 1 hour 10 minutes to clean his room and 45 minutes to clean the car. If he starts at 10.00 a.m., what time will he be finished?
11.55 a.m.

```
  10.00
 + 1.10
   0.45
  11.55
```

A car is taken in for repair at 7.30 a.m. It is collected at 1.50 p.m., but it has been ready for collection for 30 minutes. How long did the repairs actually take?
5 hours 50 minutes

```
  13.50      6.20
 − 7.30    − 0.30
   6.20      5.50
```

Claire has to be at school by 8.50 a.m. If she takes 1 hour 30 minutes to get ready and the journey takes 35 minutes, what time does she need to get up?
6.45 a.m.

```
  1.30      8.50
 + 0.35    − 2.05
   2.05      6.45
```

A bus leaves the bus station at 8.45 a.m. and arrives back at 10.15 a.m. How long has its journey taken?
1 hour 30 minutes

```
   9.6
  10.15
 − 8.45
   1.30
```

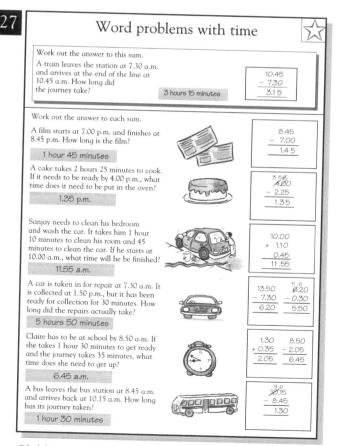

Children must remember that hours are based on units of 60 rather than of 10. e.g. in question 2, as there are 60 minutes in one hour we 'steal' a 6 rather than a 1. In question 4, a 'stolen' 6 is added to the 2 to give 80 minutes (8 in the tens column. When 3 is taken away it leaves 5.)

Frequency tables

Write the answer in the box.

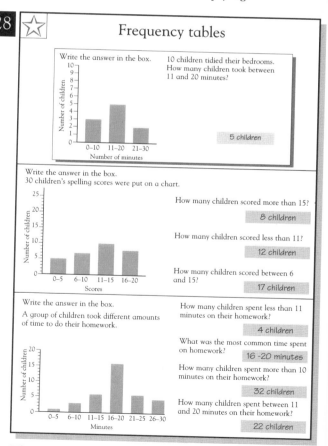

10 children tidied their bedrooms. How many children took between 11 and 20 minutes?
5 children

Write the answer in the box.
30 children's spelling scores were put on a chart.

How many children scored more than 15?
8 children

How many children scored less than 11?
12 children

How many children scored between 6 and 15?
17 children

Write the answer in the box.
A group of children took different amounts of time to do their homework.

How many children spent less than 11 minutes on their homework?
4 children

What was the most common time spent on homework?
16 -20 minutes

How many children spent more than 10 minutes on their homework?
32 children

How many children spent between 11 and 20 minutes on their homework?
22 children

This page allows children to practise reading from tables. The two most likely errors will result from mistakes in reading the table or misreading what is asked for in the question.

Probability

Mark these events on the probability line.

impossible — poor chance — even chance — good chance — certain

a) It will get dark tonight.
b) When I toss a coin it will be heads.
c) William the Conqueror will come to tea.

Mark these events on the probability line.

impossible — poor chance — even chance — good chance — certain

a) It will snow in August.
b) The sun will come up tomorrow.
c) A new baby will be a boy.
d) A dog will talk.
e) I will watch some television tonight.

HELLO!!

Now try these.

impossible — poor chance — even chance — good chance — certain

a) I will roll a six on a dice.
b) I will not roll a six on a dice.
c) I will roll a number between one and six on a dice.
d) I will roll a seven on a dice.
e) I will either roll a one, two or three on a dice.

Mark these events on the probability line.

impossible — poor chance — even chance — good chance — certain

a) I will drink something today.
b) If I drop my book, it will fall face down.
c) The next book I read will have exactly 100 pages.
d) It will rain orange squash tomorrow.
e) I will see a white car today.

These examples fall fairly firmly in the categories listed. In the 1st section, children should be able to identify events categorically. As the 2nd section is based on mathematical probability, there should be no debate about the answers. There may be some discussion for the 3rd section.

Knowledge of triangles

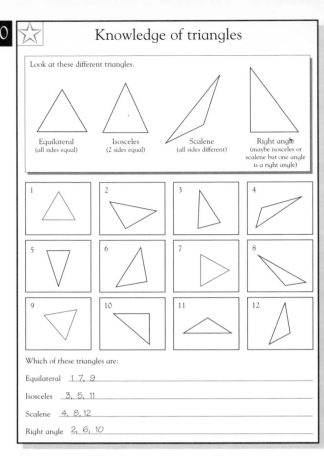

Look at these different triangles.

Equilateral (all sides equal)   Isosceles (2 sides equal)   Scalene (all sides different)   Right angle (maybe isosceles or scalene but one angle is a right angle)

1   2   3   4
5   6   7   8
9   10   11   12

Which of these triangles are:

Equilateral   1 7, 9

Isosceles   3, 5, 11

Scalene   4, 8, 12

Right angle   2, 6, 10

This page will highlight any gaps in the children's ability to recognise conventional triangle shapes. Pay close attention to whether they can identify triangles that have been rotated.

The 16-point compass

Complete the compass.

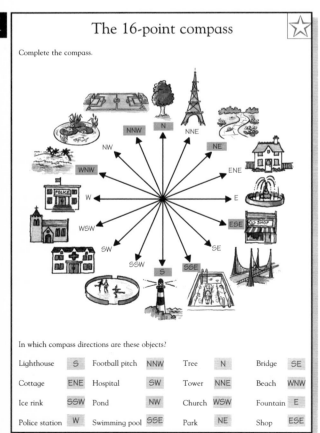

In which compass directions are these objects?

Lighthouse	S	Football pitch	NNW	Tree	N	Bridge	SE
Cottage	ENE	Hospital	SW	Tower	NNE	Beach	WNW
Ice rink	SSW	Pond	NW	Church	WSW	Fountain	E
Police station	W	Swimming pool	SSE	Park	NE	Shop	ESE

Children should be familiar with the four and eight points of the compass. If there is any confusion it is likely to be beyond this. Discussion may be necessary over the ordering of the letters for the 16-point compass.

Simple rotational symmetry

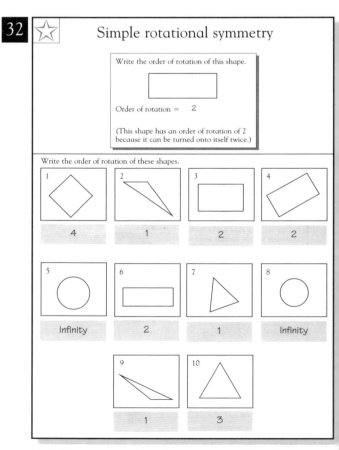

Write the order of rotation of this shape.

Order of rotation = 2

(This shape has an order of rotation of 2 because it can be turned onto itself twice.)

Write the order of rotation of these shapes.

1   4
2   1
3   2
4   2
5   Infinity
6   2
7   1
8   Infinity
9   1
10   3

If children are confused, a tracing of the shape can be fitted over the original shape to show the order of rotation. Children may not pick up on the circle which has infinite rotation, but should realise that the number will be very large. This can be discussed.

Adding decimal fractions

Write the answer in the box.

£3.35	3.45 m
+ £5.55	+ 1.25 m
£8.90	4.70 m
1	1

Write the answer in the box.

£3.60	£1.25	£7.45
+ £2.25	+ £4.55	+ £2.35

£3.60	£7.35	£5.25
+ £3.25	+ £1.45	+ £2.65

3.45 m	8.55 m	1.75 m
+ 4.35 m	+ 1.35 m	+ 5.20 m

2.40 m	7.15 m	3.85 m
+ 1.45 m	+ 1.35 m	+ 4.10 m

Write the answer in the box.

£2.75 + £4.15 =   03.75 m + 2.75 m =   £3.65 + £1.50 =

£6.25 + £1.50 =   8.65 m + 2.55 m =   £3.45 + £1.55 =

Work out the answer to each sum.

George buys two magazines that cost £2.55 and £1.75. How much does he spend?

Jennifer buys two rolls of sticky tape. One contains 7.75 m and the other contains 6.75 m. How much tape does she have altogether?

Subtracting decimal fractions

Write the answer in the box.

£6.55	4.70 m
− £3.20	− 2.50 m
£3.35	2.20 m

Write the answer in the box.

£7.45	£9.60	£5.55
− £3.30	− £7.20	− £2.40

£8.35	£3.95	£6.55
− £3.25	− £1.75	− £2.40

Write the answer in the box.

3.90 m	4.75 m	9.20 m
− 1.40 m	− 3.35 m	− 2.20 m

7.55 m	2.15 m	3.35 m
− 1.15 m	− 1.00 m	− 2.20 m

Write the answer in the box.

£4.15 − £1.10 =

£3.55 − £2.50 =

£9.75 − £4.30 =

£8.85 − £6.05 =

7.55 m − 2.30 m =

6.15 m − 4.05 m =

Work out the answer to each sum.

Khaleda has £4.65 to spend. She buys a book for £3.45. How much does she have left?

Eoin is given £9.50 for his birthday. If he spends £3.20 at the cinema how much will he have left?

Subtracting decimal fractions

Write the answer in the box.

```
   4 1
  £5.35            £7.35 m        6 1
- £2.40          - 1.65 m
 _____         _____
  £2.95            5.70 m
```

Write the answer in the box.

```
  £6.55            £7.45            £8.65
- £2.75          - £3.65          - £4.75
 _____         _____         _____


 _____         _____         _____


  £3.15            £5.70            £4.15
- £1.25          - £2.90          - £1.75
 _____         _____         _____


 _____         _____         _____
```

Write the answer in the box.

```
  5.35 m           7.25 m           4.15 m
- 2.55 m         - 2.55 m         - 2.25 m
 _____         _____         _____


 _____         _____         _____


  5.45 m           8.15 m           7.30 m
- 2.55 m         - 2.20 m         - 3.50 m
 _____         _____         _____


 _____         _____         _____
```

Write the answer in the box.

£6.25 – £2.50   =   £4.35 – £2.55   =

£5.20 – £3.30   =   £7.40 – £3.80   =

6.45 m – 2.55 m   =   7.35 m – 3.55 m =

Work out the answer to each sum.

Kevin has a piece of wood 4.55 m long. He cuts off a piece
1.65 m long. How much does he have left?

Abir's long jump result is 2.35 m. Steven's is 1.40 m. How much
longer is Abir's jump than Steven's?

Multiplying by units

Complete these sums.

32	26	34
x 2	x 3	x 4
64	78	136
	1	1

Complete these sums.

27	32	16	19
x 2	x 3	x 4	x 2
4	6	4	8

22	25	18	33
x 3	x 4	x 6	x 5
6	0	8	5

39	26	41	38
x 2	x 2	x 2	x 3

29	45	28	16
x 3	x 2	x 3	x 6

10	40	20	50
x 5	x 2	x 4	x 3

Work out the answer to each sum.

Laura has 36 marbles but Sarah has twice as many. How many marbles does Sarah have?

A ruler is 30 cm long.
How long will 4 rulers be?

Multiplying by units

Complete these sums.

```
    53          76          25
  x  3        x  6        x  7
  -----       -----       -----
   159         456         175
                3           3
```

Complete these sums.

```
    56          46          32          36
  x  8        x  7        x  6        x  9
  -----       -----       -----       -----
    8           2           2           4
```

```
    45          73          96          58
  x  4        x  5        x  3        x  7
  -----       -----       -----       -----
    0           5           8           6
```

```
    33      48          24      19          64      52
  x  6    x  5        x  9    x  8        x  4    x  6
  -----   -----       -----   -----       -----   -----
```

```
    81      37          40      50          30      20
  x  3    x  7        x  8    x  3        x  7    x  9
  -----   -----       -----   -----       -----   -----
```

Work out the answer to each sum.

A school coach holds 36 children.
How many children can you
get in 6 coach loads?

28 children bring 7 comics each
to school. How many comics do
they have altogether?

21

Division with fraction remainders

Work out these division sums.

$$5\frac{1}{3}$$ $$6\frac{2}{4} = 6\frac{1}{2}$$

$$3\overline{\smash{\big)}16}$$ $$4\overline{\smash{\big)}26}$$

Remember you may need to simplify your answer.

Work out these division sums. Part of the answer has been done for you.

$$2\overline{\smash{\big)}15} \quad \frac{}{2}$$
$$4\overline{\smash{\big)}17} \quad \frac{}{4}$$
$$3\overline{\smash{\big)}19} \quad \frac{}{3}$$

$$4\overline{\smash{\big)}25} \quad \frac{}{4}$$
$$2\overline{\smash{\big)}21} \quad \frac{}{2}$$
$$3\overline{\smash{\big)}43} \quad \frac{}{3}$$

$$4\overline{\smash{\big)}87} \quad \frac{}{4}$$
$$2\overline{\smash{\big)}39} \quad \frac{}{2}$$
$$3\overline{\smash{\big)}59} \quad \frac{}{3}$$

Now try these.

$$2\overline{\smash{\big)}35}$$ $$4\overline{\smash{\big)}46}$$ $$3\overline{\smash{\big)}22}$$ $$5\overline{\smash{\big)}49}$$

$$4\overline{\smash{\big)}58}$$ $$5\overline{\smash{\big)}63}$$ $$5\overline{\smash{\big)}37}$$ $$4\overline{\smash{\big)}50}$$

$$3\overline{\smash{\big)}76}$$ $$4\overline{\smash{\big)}58}$$ $$5\overline{\smash{\big)}94}$$ $$5\overline{\smash{\big)}83}$$

$$2\overline{\smash{\big)}99}$$ $$4\overline{\smash{\big)}75}$$ $$5\overline{\smash{\big)}77}$$ $$2\overline{\smash{\big)}37}$$

Write the answer in the box.

What is 27 divided by 4?   Divide 78 by 5.

What is 46 divided by 3?   Divide 63 by 2.

Division with fraction remainders

Work out these division sums.

$$5\frac{4}{6} = 5\frac{2}{3} \qquad 7\frac{1}{7}$$

$$6\overline{)34} \qquad\qquad 7\overline{)50}$$

Remember you may need to simplify your answer.

Work out these division sums. Part of the answer has been done for you.

$6\overline{)73}^{\ \overline{6}}$ $\qquad$ $7\overline{)81}^{\ \overline{7}}$ $\qquad$ $8\overline{)93}^{\ \overline{8}}$

$9\overline{)92}^{\ \overline{9}}$ $\qquad$ $8\overline{)65}^{\ \overline{8}}$ $\qquad$ $7\overline{)90}^{\ \overline{7}}$

$9\overline{)47}^{\ \overline{9}}$ $\qquad$ $7\overline{)36}^{\ \overline{7}}$ $\qquad$ $6\overline{)83}^{\ \overline{6}}$

Now try these.

$6\overline{)99}$ $\qquad$ $6\overline{)43}$ $\qquad$ $9\overline{)30}$ $\qquad$ $8\overline{)76}$

$7\overline{)52}$ $\qquad$ $7\overline{)83}$ $\qquad$ $9\overline{)52}$ $\qquad$ $6\overline{)91}$

$7\overline{)66}$ $\qquad$ $8\overline{)63}$ $\qquad$ $6\overline{)27}$ $\qquad$ $8\overline{)46}$

$9\overline{)93}$ $\qquad$ $7\overline{)85}$ $\qquad$ $8\overline{)67}$ $\qquad$ $7\overline{)26}$

Write the answer in the box.

What is 85 divided by 7? $\qquad$ Divide 84 by 8.

What is 75 divided by 6? $\qquad$ Divide 73 by 9.

Real life problems

Write the answer in the box.

Yasmin has £4.60 and she is given another £1.20.
How much does she have?

> £5.80

$$
\begin{array}{r}
£4.60 \\
+ £1.20 \\
\hline
£5.80
\end{array}
$$

David has 12 packets of sweets.
He gives them to his 5 friends.
How many packets
do they each get?

$2\frac{2}{5}$

$2\frac{2}{5}$

$5\overline{)12}$

Write the answer in the box.

Michael buys a ball for £5.50 and a torch for £3.65.
How much does he spend?

5.50
3.65
10'.5

£9.15

How much does he have left from £10?

0.85p.

A class of 32 children bring in £5 each for a school trip.
What is the total amount brought in?   32×5

£160

A set of 5 shelves can be made from a piece of wood 4 m long.
What fraction of a metre will each shelf be?

5 children have £16 each.
How much do they have altogether?

If the above total was shared between 8 children how much would
each child have then?

Real life problems

Work out the answer to each sum.

A box is 16 cm wide. How wide will 6 boxes be if placed together?

96 cm

A box is 16 cm wide. How wide will 6 boxes be if placed together?

$$\begin{array}{r} 16 \text{ cm} \\ \times 6 \\ \hline 96 \text{ cm} \\ \end{array}$$

3

Josh is 1.20 m tall. His sister is 1.55 m tall. How much taller than Josh is his sister?

0.35 m

$$\begin{array}{r} 1.55 \text{ m} \\ -1.20 \text{ m} \\ \hline 0.35 \text{ m} \\ \end{array}$$

Work out the answer to each sum.

A tin contains 56 g of gravy powder. If 12 g are used, how much is left?

A large jar of coffee weighs 280 g. A smaller jar weighs 130 g. How much heavier is the larger jar than the smaller jar?

There are 7 shelves of books. 5 shelves are 1.2 m long. 2 shelves are 1.5 m long. What is the total length of the 7 shelves?

A pop star can sign 36 photographs in a minute. How many can he sign in 30 seconds?

Natalie has read 5 pages of a 20-page comic. If it has taken her 9 minutes, how long is it likely to take her to read the whole comic?

Area of rectangles and squares

★

Find the area of this rectangle.

5 cm

| 15 | cm² |

3 cm

To find the area of a rectangle or square we multiply length (l) by width (w).
Area = l x w = 5 cm x 3 cm = 15 cm²

Find the area of these rectangles and squares.

2 cm

5 cm

☐ cm²

4 cm

4 cm

☐ cm²

3 cm

8 cm

☐ cm²

2 cm

2 cm

☐ cm²

7 cm

2 cm

☐ cm²

3 cm

9 cm

☐ cm²

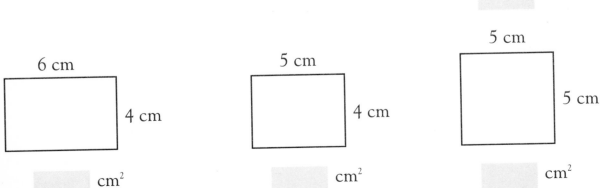

6 cm

4 cm

☐ cm²

5 cm

4 cm

☐ cm²

5 cm

5 cm

☐ cm²

Word problems with time

Work out the answer to this sum.

A train leaves the station at 7.30 a.m. and arrives at the end of the line at 10.45 a.m. How long did the journey take?

3 hours 15 minutes

```
  10.45
-  7.30
  3.15
```

Work out the answer to each sum.

A film starts at 7.00 p.m. and finishes at 8.45 p.m. How long is the film?

A cake takes 2 hours 25 minutes to cook. If it needs to be ready by 4.00 p.m., what time does it need to be put in the oven?

Sanjay needs to clean his bedroom and wash the car. It takes him 1 hour 10 minutes to clean his room and 45 minutes to clean the car. If he starts at 10.00 a.m., what time will he be finished?

A car is taken in for repair at 7.30 a.m. It is collected at 1.50 p.m., but it has been ready for collection for 30 minutes. How long did the repairs actually take?

Claire has to be at school by 8.50 a.m. If she takes 1 hour 30 minutes to get ready and the journey takes 35 minutes, what time does she need to get up?

A bus leaves the bus station at 8.45 a.m. and arrives back at 10.15 a.m. How long has its journey taken?

Frequency tables

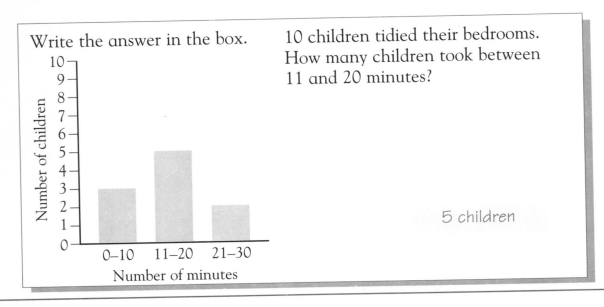

Write the answer in the box.

10 children tidied their bedrooms. How many children took between 11 and 20 minutes?

5 children

Write the answer in the box.

30 children's spelling scores were put on a chart.

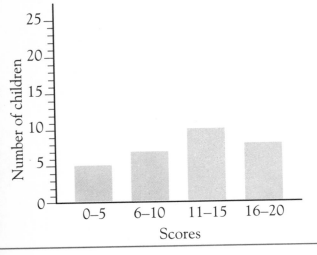

How many children scored more than 15?

How many children scored less than 11?

How many children scored between 6 and 15?

Write the answer in the box.

A group of children took different amounts of time to do their homework.

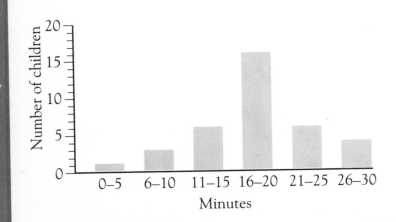

How many children spent less than 11 minutes on their homework?

What was the most common time spent on homework?

How many children spent more than 10 minutes on their homework?

How many children spent between 11 and 20 minutes on their homework?

Probability

Mark these events on the probability line.

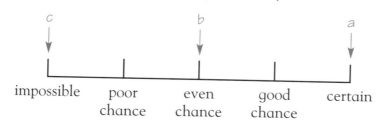

impossible   poor   even   good   certain
      chance   chance   chance

a) It will get dark tonight.
b) When I toss a coin it will be heads.
c) William the Conqueror will come to tea.

Mark these events on the probability line.

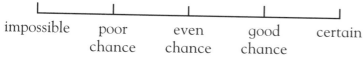

impossible   poor   even   good   certain
      chance   chance   chance

a) It will snow in August.
b) The sun will come up tomorrow.
c) A new baby will be a boy.
d) A dog will talk.
e) I will watch some television tonight.

Now try these.

impossible   poor   even   good   certain
      chance   chance   chance

a) I will roll a six on a dice.
b) I will not roll a six on a dice.
c) I will roll a number between one and six on a dice.
d) I will roll a seven on a dice.
e) I will either roll a one, two or three on a dice.

Mark these events on the probability line.

impossible   poor   even   good   certain
      chance   chance   chance

a) I will drink something today.
b) If I drop my book, it will fall face down.
c) The next book I read will have exactly 100 pages.
d) It will rain orange squash tomorrow.
e) I will see a white car today.

Knowledge of triangles

Look at these different triangles.

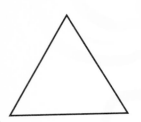 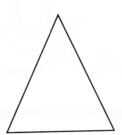 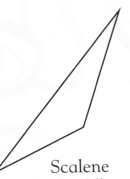 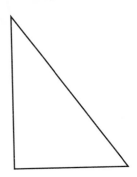

Equilateral
(all sides equal)

Isosceles
(2 sides equal)

Scalene
(all sides different)

Right angle
(maybe isosceles or scalene but one angle is a right angle)

1 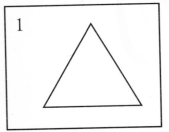	2 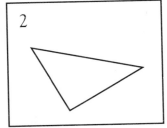	3 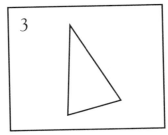	4 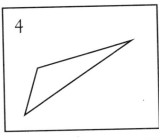
5 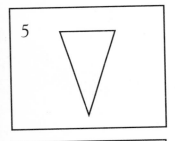	6 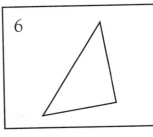	7 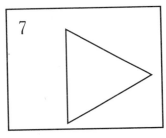	8 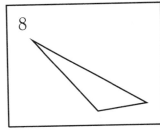
9 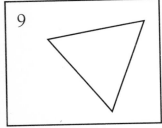	10 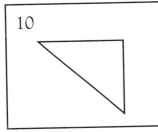	11 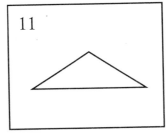	12 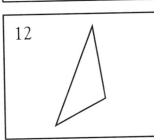

Which of these triangles are:

Equilateral _____

Isosceles _____

Scalene _____

Right angle _____

30

The 16-point compass

Complete the compass.

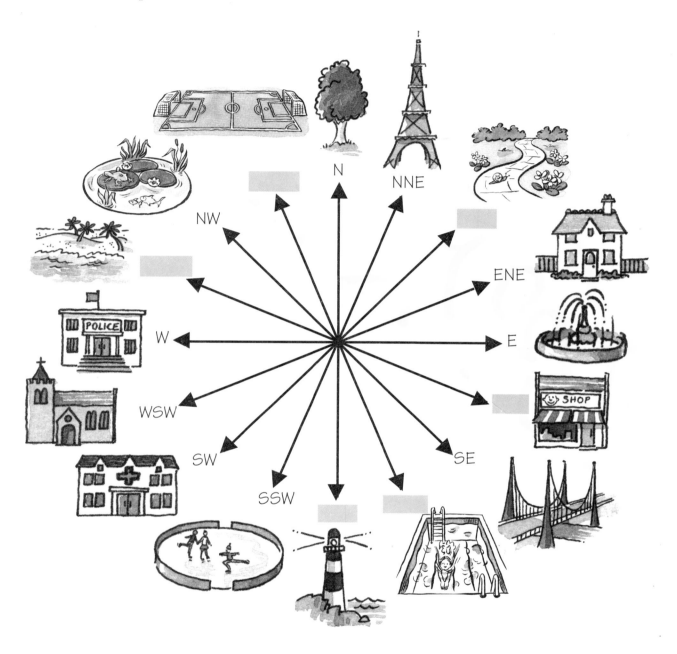

In which compass directions are these objects?

Lighthouse	S	Football pitch		Tree		Bridge
Cottage	ENE	Hospital		Tower		Beach
Ice rink		Pond		Church		Fountain
Police station		Swimming pool		Park		Shop

Simple rotational symmetry

Write the order of rotation of this shape.

Order of rotation = 2

(This shape has an order of rotation of 2 because it can be turned onto itself twice.)

Write the order of rotation of these shapes.

1	2	3	4
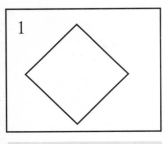	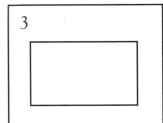	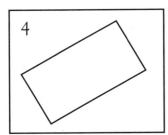	

5	6	7	8
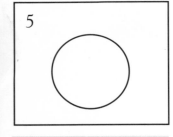	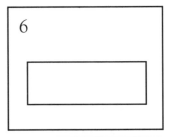	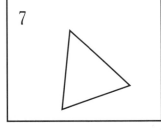	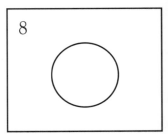

9	10
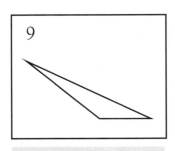	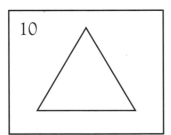